VIOLIN

Preliminary Studies

Open strings, first, second and third fingers

HERBERT KINSEY

**The Associated Board
of the Royal Schools of Music**

VIOLIN

TWELVE PRELIMINARY STUDIES

OPEN STRINGS, 1st, 2nd and 3rd FINGERS

HERBERT KINSEY

1

2

A.B. 924

3

4

5

The 1st Finger

6

The 1st Finger

7
The 1st Finger

8

The 1st and 2nd Fingers

(Whole Tones)

8

9

The 1st and 2nd Fingers

(Semitones between 1st and 2nd)

10

The 1st and 2nd Fingers

(Whole Tones)

11
The 1st, 2nd and 3rd Fingers
(Semitones between 2nd and 3rd)

12
The 1st, 2nd and 3rd Fingers
(Whole Tones between 2nd and 3rd)

Andante con moto